Go to b

Katie Carr

National Literacy Strategy

Encourage your child to recognize these essential words
as you read this story:

at   bed   but   go   in   is   look

no   not   to   up   yes

Go up to bed, Ben.

Is Ben in bed?

No, Ben is not in bed!

Go to bed, Ben.

Is Ben in bed?

Yes, Ben is in bed.

But look at Ben!

Run away!

Katie Carr

Robber Red met a rat.

The rat ran away.

Robber Red met a rabbit.

The rabbit ran away.

Robber Red met a man.

The man did not run away!

Robber Red ran away!

Lots of hats

Lyn Wendon

National Literacy Strategy
Encourage your child to recognize these essential words
as you read this story:

a   and   cat   for   has   he   man
of   that   the

The Hat Man has lots of hats.

He has hats for hens.

He has hats for cats ...

and hats for rats.

He has hats for bats.

He has hats for hippos …

... and a hat that's flat!

Bad dog!

Katie Carr

National Literacy Strategy

Encourage your child to recognize these essential words
as you read this story:

and   but   come   dad   dog   like
me   play   to

Nick and Nip like to play.

But Nip likes to dig!

Nip digs and digs.

"Bad dog," says Nick.

"Come to me, Nip," says Dad.

"Sit, Nip," says Dad.

Nip sits!